Let's Play Peek-a-Boo

By Joan Webb
Illustrated by Kim Mulkey

A GOLDEN BOOK, NEW YORK
Western Publishing Company, Inc., Racine, Wisconsin 53404

Sarah and her brother Tim like to play games.
They play pat-a-cake,

and follow-the-leader,

and "How big are you?"

But Sarah's favorite game
is peek-a-boo.

They hide behind the door

and play peek-a-boo with Mommy.

They hide behind the chair

and play peek-a-boo with puppy.

They play peek-a-boo at bedtime.

They play peek-a-boo outside.

Daddy likes to play. . .

and Grandpa likes to play.

Would you like to play, too?

Can you find Sarah and Tim?

Now where are they hiding?

Can you find them? Look and see.

Peek-a-boo here and peek-a-boo there,
it's fun to play peek-a-boo everywhere!